Literacy Support

Unit 3 - Book B

Text Level Work (NC Levels 2-3)

Comprehension and Composition

William Hartley

Illustrated by Peter Rigg

Contents

Check-up tests for the above sections can be found in Book D

Name: _____

Riddles

A **riddle** is a puzzling question.

How ...? **What** ...? **When** ...? **Where** ...? and **Why** ...? are often, but not always, the beginnings for riddles.

What is the best way to make trousers last? *Make the coat first.*

1. Connect each **riddle** to its answer.

| What kind of coat should be put on when it is wet? |
| Why does a sheep go over a hill? |
| When is a car not a car? |
| How can you tell which end of a worm is which? |
| Where do bulls get their messages? |

| On a bulletin board. |
| Tickle it in the middle and see which end laughs. |
| A coat of paint. |
| When it turns into a road. |
| It's because a sheep cannot go under a hill. |

2. Write the answer to this **riddle**.

Which will burn longer:
the candles on the birthday cake of a boy, or
the candles on the birthday cake of a girl?

_____

3. Find five more **riddles**.
Write them with their answers.
Test the **riddles** on some of your friends.

Mark

Amusing stories

A short and amusing story about a single event is called an **anecdote**.

is usually amusing

is usually about something that happened to a real person

A tricky situation

One moonlit evening, I was following a footpath through a field. Suddenly, I heard something. I looked over my shoulder and saw a large goat charging towards me. I ran to a nearby oak tree and climbed into its lower branches.

The goat was below me looking up. How could I escape?

Two hours passed and the goat wandered off. I took my chance and I climbed down the tree. I rushed to the gate and leapt over it into a lane. I was only just in time! The goat was already on the other side looking at me and pawing the ground.

I laughed to myself and started to walk along the lane.

Suddenly, I heard something. Another goat was chasing after me.

Write an anecdote about something that happened to you.

_____

_____

_____

_____

_____

_____

Mark

2

Name: _____

Argument text

The style of writing below is called **argument** text.
Read it and then answer the questions.

has an opening statement

gives a point of view, reasons
or evidence for the argument

Exercise is important

Taking exercise is one of the best ways of keeping fit.

Exercise makes your body strong. A strong body means that your muscles can work hard without you getting out of breath.

Things like walking, running and taking part in games are all good ways of getting exercise. Exercise also makes your heart stronger, helps you to keep your weight down and stretches your joints, making them stronger and more supple.

So, I think you will agree, regular exercise is one of the best ways of helping someone to live a long and healthy life.

has a closing statement

1. What is one of the best ways of keeping fit?

   _____

2. What does a strong body allow you to do?

   _____

3. Write three ways of getting exercise mentioned in the passage.

   _____

   _____

   _____

4. Write six other ways of exercising your body.

Mark

Letter writing 1

> The type of writing below is called a **note**.
> It is used to leave a quick message for someone.

(has a chatty style)   (uses short sentences and simple language)   (has no address or date)

Mum

I'm off out on my bike with Kez. Not going far. I'll finish my homework when I get back. Should be about 8 o'clock. If Jenny rings tell her I'll call her tomorrow.

Annum

(ends with just the writer's first name)

Write a note to a friend in the same chatty style as Annum's note.

Mark

Newsletters

Newsletters are sent by clubs and societies to let their members know what is going on. Schools often send newsletters to parents.

Lowton High School, Moor Lane, HELSTON, HL5 4NY

Head teacher: Mrs J Fussy

Tel: 0173 665298

(who is involved) (type of event) (where and when)

Dear Parents,

The Year 10 play this year is a comedy called The Secret House. It takes place in the school hall on Friday 19th November starting at 7.00 pm. Refreshments will be on sale in the library during the interval. The cost per ticket is £1.50 and tickets are on sale now at the school office.

Yours sincerely,

(anything else important)

J Fussy

Jane Fussy (Head teacher)

Imagine your school is organising a car boot sale. Write a newsletter for all the parents telling them about the car boot sale.

Include:

- the address of the school.
- the type of event.
- who is taking part.
- when and where it is happening.
- other important information.

Mark ☐

⑤

Instruction text

The style of writing below is called instruction text. Read it and then answer the questions.

says what you need

tells how to do something

Pond dipping
You need: net, plastic box, spoon, bucket
What to do: visit a pond with your teacher and:

has action verbs

1. Fill the bucket with water.
2. Dip the net into the pond.
3. Pull it out and put it in the bucket.
4. Turn it inside out in the water.
5. Look to see what you have caught.

states in what order to do things

1. How many items are used to go pond dipping?

_____

2. Into which container do you put water?

_____

3. Why do you turn the net inside out in the bucket of water?

_____

4. What should you do with any animals you do not wish to study later?

_____

Mark

Letter writing 2

This is how you write a letter to someone you know but don't meet very often.

Read it and then make up an ending in your own words.

has the writer's address and the date

uses first names

28 Pier Road
BRIGHTON
BG6 5ZX
14th May 2004

Dear Sarah

I am sorry to hear that you fell off your bike and broke your leg. Ice on the road is always a problem. Think yourself lucky that you didn't get run over by a car.

I know you won't be able to take part in the fun run. Not to worry, you'll soon be up and running again.

Yesterday, I was in the High Street texting my friend and not looking where I was going. I walked into a lamp post and cut my head open. I had to go to hospital and had five stitches. Would you believe it?

_____

_____

_____

_____

_____

All the best

has a friendly closing _____ uses first names

Mark

Drama text

The style of writing below is called **drama** text.
It is used for plays and film scripts.
Make up an ending to this play.

(*Three teenagers leaving through the front door of a leisure centre after having had a swim. Heavy rain falling outside.*)

speaker's name

scene setting sentences

KELLY: What now? Do you fancy a coffee?

PAT: Good idea. Let's go to Drinkits.

DAVE: OK, that's where Joe hangs out.

words state what the speaker actually says

KELLY: Who's Joe?

DAVE: My cousin. He'll probably pay for our coffee!

KELLY: Great! Let's go!

(*Suddenly there is a screech of car tyres.*)

DAVE: Look out Kelly.

KELLY: _____

PAT: _____

KELLY: _____

PAT: _____

DAVE: _____

KELLY: _____

PAT: _____

Mark

Report text

The type of writing below is called **report** text.
Read it and then answer the questions.

Solids, liquids and gases

is usually about one thing

This week, at school we have been learning about the differences between solids, liquids and gases.

Everything is made of matter which can be either a solid, a liquid or a gas.

A solid has a fixed shape and a fixed size - for example, a brick. A liquid has a fixed size but no fixed shape - for example, milk in a carton. A gas has neither a fixed shape or a fixed size - for example, air in a balloon.

usually has facts and drawings to support the subject

solid   liquid   gas

1. What is everything made of? _____

2. Name the three states in which matter is found.

_____   _____   _____

3. Write two examples of each of these materials.

solid	liquid	gas

4. Describe a:

a) solid   b) liquid   c) gas

Letter writing 3

This is how to set out a **letter** to someone you do not know and have never met.

$\qquad$ your address $\qquad$

31 School Lane
EXETER
EX65 4SB

Woodside Camp Site
Littleton
NORWICH
NR5 1ST

address where the letter is going

16th July 2004 — the date

Dear Sir/Madam — start with this greeting

I would like to book a pitch on your camp site for a small ridge tent with two occupants.
We wish to stay for five nights. We will be arriving in the late afternoon of Monday, 3rd August and leaving in the morning of Saturday, 8th August.
Will you please let me know by letter if you have space available on your site for the nights mentioned above.

Yours faithfully — close with this ending

R Johnson — your signature

Robert Johnson — your full name

Write a **letter** asking a mail order camping shop to send you a price list for their range of hiking boots.

Mark ☐ (10)

Paragraphs

Paragraphs are used to make writing easier to read. They are made up of a sentence or group of sentences which **focus** on one thing. Very often the first sentence is a **topic** sentence telling you what the paragraph is about.

> Para 1: focus on Lee Bell

Para 1	Lee Bell is thirty-five years old and has brown hair and blue eyes.
Para 2	He lives in a stone-built house with a red roof. It is very comfortable and has plenty of space for his family.
Para 3	There are four bedrooms and a bathroom upstairs. Lee and his wife sleep in the front bedroom and their two children have a bedroom each. The other bedroom is used by friends who come to stay.

> Para 2: focus on his house   Para 3: focus on the upstairs

1. Here is the next **paragraph** about Lee Bell's house but the sentences are not in the correct order.
   Write them in the correct order so that the paragraph makes better sense.

Both are large and square. The living room is used the most by the family. Mrs Bell says that her favourite room is the kitchen. The downstairs has a living room and a kitchen with a dining area.

_____

_____

_____

_____

---

2. Make up a three sentence **paragraph** saying what you think Mr Bell's garden might look like.

Mark

11

Explanation text

The type of writing below is called **explanation** text.
Read it and then answer the questions.

describes how something works

How the water cycle works
The water cycle is the movement of water around the Earth.
Heat from the Sun turns water from the sea into water vapour. Water vapour is a gas which forms clouds. Clouds are blown by the wind over the land. They cool and turn into water which falls as rain.
Sometimes, if it is very cold, the water in clouds will freeze and fall as sleet, hail or snow. Once on the land, the rain water, or melted sleet, hail or snow, flows back to the sea and the cycle begins all over again.

often describes a series of steps in a definite order   has facts

1. Answer these questions in complete sentences.

    a) What is the water cycle?

    _____

    b) What does water vapour form in the sky?

    _____

    c) How do clouds move from over the sea to over the land?

    _____

2. Name three forms of water that fall from the clouds.

    _____   _____   _____

3. How does most rain water get back to the sea?

    _____

Mark

12

Alliteration

Sometimes nearby words in a sentence, **start** with the same consonant sound. This is called **alliteration**.

The <u>h</u>orrible <u>h</u>at was <u>h</u>ugging <u>h</u>er <u>h</u>ead.

1. Add another word that **alliterates** with the three already there.

violin	volcano	vowel	
camera	cabbage	cottage	
gaze	gather	grateful	
listen	lettuce	library	

2. Underline the letters that **alliterate** in these sentences.

Lenny, the lazy lion, looked lost.

Dozy Donald dug a very deep ditch.

Nine noisy neighbours nattering about nothing.

3. Use the words in the box to fill in the gaps in this passage.

swiftly	floats	house	rod	jumped

Henry hurried home to his _____. He swapped his sweaters

_____. Then _____ into his jeans. He rushed with

his _____ to the river. On the bank sat five fat fishermen

fiddling with their _____.

Mark

Fact or fiction?

RSPB Guide to
British Birds
by D Saunders

David Copperfield
by C Dickens

Writing that is **true** is called **fact**.
It has **not been invented** by its author.

Writing that is **untrue** is called **fiction**.
It has **been invented** by its author.

1. Write something **true** that happened to you.

_____

_____

_____

_____

_____

_____

2. Make up a short piece of **fictional** writing.

_____

_____

_____

_____

_____

_____

_____

Mark

Recount text

The style of writing below is called **recount** text.
Read it and then answer the questions.

has action verbs

has facts

Our Journey to Anglesey

We left home at 8 am. The weather was warm and sunny with no clouds in the sky.
We drove north on the M6 and then west on the M54. At Telford we parked in a
lay-by for a picnic lunch. I ate three sandwiches and a yogurt. Boxer was hungry,
too, so we opened a can of meat and gave him some water.

When we set off again we followed the A5 and drove through the beautiful Welsh
valleys towards Anglesey. We crossed the Menai Bridge, which connects mainland
Wales to the island of Anglesey. At last we arrived at our cottage at 4 pm ready
for our holiday to begin. I was very excited.

states in what order things are done

often uses 'I' and 'we'

1. Which type of transport did the family use to travel to Anglesey?

   _____

2. What did the writer eat for lunch at Telford?

   _____

3. Who or what is Boxer?

   _____

4. Is Anglesey part of mainland Wales or is it a separate island?

   _____

5. How long would their journey from home to the cottage have taken if
   they had been delayed two hours in a traffic jam?

   _____

Mark

Name: _____

Leaflets

A **leaflet** is a sheet of paper. It is sometimes used to advertise products and events and is often given away free of charge.

It is similar to a newsletter but has a more eye-catching and exciting layout and often uses pictures to attract people's attention.

1. Plan a parents **leaflet** advertising your school pantomime.
    The idea of the leaflet is to get as many parents as possible to come.

Include: ⟶ (the name of the pantomime) ⟶ (who is involved)

(anything else important) ⟵ (the cost) ⟵ (where and when)

Planning notes

1. _____

2. _____

3. _____

4. _____

5. _____

2. Now make the **leaflet** on a separate piece of paper.

Mark

Blurbs and advertisements

If you look on the back cover of a book you will sometimes find some facts that tell you what the book is about. These facts are called a **blurb**.

Most **advertisements** are also a kind of blurb. They let you know about things that are going to happen or items that are for sale.

The Best Joke Book Ever
Full of rib-tickling, gut-busting jokes to amuse you and your friends for hours and hours - an absolute must!

Rock Solid Furniture Ltd. Massive sale with low, low prices! Call us today for tables, chairs, beds ... Tel: 01998 340729

1. Find a book with a **blurb** on the back cover.
   Below, write what the blurb says about the book.

2. Write an **advertisement** for a computer you have for sale.
   Think very carefully about the information you need to include.

_____

_____

_____

_____

Mark

Name: _____

Narrative text

The style of writing below is called **narrative** (story) text. Narrative text usually has a **beginning** Ⓑ, a **middle** Ⓜ and an **end** Ⓔ. Read the text and then answer the questions.

《 involves people 》   《 usually has a problem in it 》

Stuck in a Lift

Ⓑ Amy and Mariya entered the lift in the shopping centre. They pressed the button and the lift moved upwards.

Ⓜ Suddenly it stopped with a noisy, grinding lurch.
'What's happened?' asked Mariya.
'I don't know,' said Amy.   《 has speech in it 》
They waited and they waited but nothing happened.
Together they both shouted, 'Help! Help!'

Ⓔ With a jerk, the lift slowly began to move again. Finally it stopped, the doors opened, and the girls stepped out.
'Let's use the stairs when we go down,' said Amy.
'You can say that again,' replied Mariya.

《 usually ends with the problem solved 》

---

1. In which direction did the lift move when the button was pressed?

_____

2. Describe how the lift stopped.

_____

3. Do you think the children went back down in the lift? Give a reason.

_____

4. What would you do if the same thing happened to you?

_____

Mark

Story boards

A **story board** is a set of pictures used to plan a story.
The pictures show what is happening in the story.

Look carefully at this **story board**.

Trouble with the Weather | story board

Write a story to go with the pictures.

Mark

Redrafting

A good story is never correct the first time it is written. It has to be worked upon and made better. This is called **redrafting**.

You will need your Trouble with the Weather story from the Story board worksheet.

Read your story called Trouble with the Weather.
Look for ways you can make it better.
Then **redraft** the story in the space below.

Trouble with the Weather

_____

_____

_____

_____

_____

_____

_____

_____

_____

Mark

Life stories 1

A **life story** of a person written by that person is called an **autobiography**. An example of this style is given below.

written in the 1st person

This is my life

My name is John Gibson. I was born in Mount Street Hospital, York on Monday 21st April 1980.

My mother told me I was the noisiest baby she had ever met. This may be true, but I was too young to remember.

At the age of four, I started at a school which was a mile away from home. The school was great. I had no brothers or sisters, so for the first time in my life I had other boys and girls to play with. I enjoyed all subjects but sport was my favourite.

Mr Race was a teacher at the school. He noticed that I had the ability to become a sprinting superstar. He spent hours and hours helping me.

1. a) Whose **life story** begins in the box above? _____

   b) Where was the writer born? _____

   c) When was the writer born? _____

2. Why can the writer not remember if he was a noisy baby?

   _____

3. Why did the writer find playing with other children so enjoyable?

   _____

4. Who was Mr Race?

   _____

5. Suggest ways in which Mr Race might have helped the writer to become a champion sprinter.

   _____

Mark

Writing frames

A **writing frame** is a set of questions used to plan a story. It makes you think about the story before writing it.

Answer the questions in this **writing frame**, as if you are going to write a story.

What is the title of the story?

_____

Who is in the story?

_____

What are they going to do?

_____

_____

Where is it going to happen?

_____

_____

What happens next?

_____

_____

How will the story end?

_____

_____

Mark

Editing

Before writers can have their work printed someone else has to check it for mistakes. Doing this is called **editing**.

Edit each piece of writing by circling the mistakes. Then write each piece correctly in the space below. Look for incorrect facts and errors in grammar.

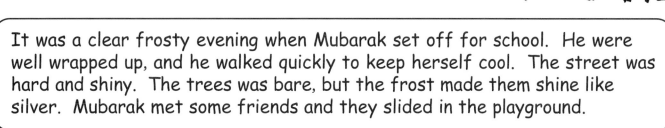

It was a clear frosty evening when Mubarak set off for school. He were well wrapped up, and he walked quickly to keep herself cool. The street was hard and shiny. The trees was bare, but the frost made them shine like silver. Mubarak met some friends and they slided in the playground.

A magnet is a piece of iron or steel that have an unseen force that can make items made of wood or plastic move. The force is called gravity. The force of a magnet is strongest at its poles. The poles are at the ends of a magnet. One end is called the north pole and the other end is called the east pole.

Life stories 2

A **life story** of a person written by another person is called a **biography**. An example of this style of writing is given below.

is usually written in the 3rd person

From there to here

Emma Smith, our local countryside ranger, was born in Devon on 19th June, 1974. She went to Dunnock Primary - a small school with only three classes.

In 1985 she moved to Mallory High School. Her interest in the countryside started there and she did well in biology and environmental studies. Her work in the school garden made the school well known for its vegetable plot.

She left Mallory High at sixteen to work at the garden centre looking after the outdoor plants. After six years at the garden centre she saw an advert to be a countryside ranger.

1. a) Whose **life story** begins in the box above? _____

    b) Where was she born? _____

    c) When was she born? _____

2. Describe Dunnock Primary School.

_____

3. When did she become interested in the countryside?

_____

4. How did Emma's work make Mallory High School well-known?

_____

5. Why do you think Emma applied for the countryside ranger job?

_____

Mark

Proof-reading

Before writers can have their work printed, someone else must check it for spelling and punctuation mistakes. Doing this is called **proof-reading**.

Here is the start of a story about a girl called Matilda.
Proof-read it and circle the mistakes.
Then rewrite it correctly on the lines below.

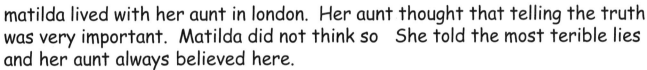

matilda lived with her aunt in london. Her aunt thought that telling the truth was very important. Matilda did not think so   She told the most terible lies and her aunt always believed here.
Late won afternoon her aunt had gone out. Matilda, being bored with playing, krept up to the telephone and dailled 999.
'hello, can I speak to the fire brigade 'she asked. 'My name is Matilda. Come quickly the house is on fire.
Soon four different fire engines were rushing two Matildas' house

_____

_____

_____

_____

_____

_____

_____

Mark

 **E-mails**

The message below is an **e-mail**. It is typed straight into a computer and sent electronically to someone else. Most e-mails are written in the way you would write to a good friend or someone you know very well.

Jean Smith

From: Sam Hodder <samhodder@hellohello.co.uk>

To: Jean Smith <jean@swapmail.co.uk>

Sent: 14 June 2005 10:25

Subject: A bit of a problem!

sender's details

Jean

has a chatty style

Will be late getting to your house. The car won't start. The AA should be here in about an hour. If you've gone when I arrive I will go to the camp site. Don't panic! See you when I see you.

Sam

uses shortish sentences and simple words

Write an **e-mail** to a friend in a chatty style like Sam's e-mail. Write only the message.

Name: _____

Poetry text

The type of writing below is called **poetry** text.

The Silent Snake
The birds go fluttering in the air,
The rabbits run and skip,
Grey squirrels race along the bough,
The May flies rise and dip;
But, whilst these creatures play and leap,
The silent snake goes creepy-creep!
Anon

often has words that rhyme

uses words to create pictures in your mind

1. Look up the meaning of the word creatures and write it down.

_____

2. a) How many types of creatures are mentioned in the poem? _____

   b) Write their names. _____

3. How is the snake different from the other creatures?

_____

4. What picture is created in your mind by the line
   'Grey squirrels race along the bough.'

_____

_____

5. Which other word in the poem rhymes with creep? _____

6. Anon is short for anonymous. Find out what anonymous means.

_____

Mark [ ] 27

Literacy Support - Unit 3 - Text Level Work - Book B

Additional information for teachers

1	For more riddles to use with the class visit one of the many 'riddles' websites. If you don't have the time, here are a couple more you can use: Q - What kind of animal eats with its tail? A - All kinds of animals eat with tails. They can't take them off. Q - What is the hardest thing about learning to ride a bicycle? A - The thing you fall on.
2	Ask for volunteer pupils to read out some of the anecdotes they have written on the worksheet. Discuss with the class which of these anecdotes best meet the requirements for an anecdote as outlined on the worksheet. Mention to the pupils that older people often use anecdotes as a way of warning children against courses of action that were unsuccessful for themselves in the past.
3	This is a difficult genre of writing for pupils with special needs to understand. Try to reinforce the four main features of its structure as given on the worksheet, namely: it puts forward a point of view, it has an opening statement, it has a series of reasons or evidence for the argument which may include details and facts and it has a closing statement which sums up the argument.
4	Reinforce the basic characteristics of a note, namely: it is only used when writing a message to a good friend or somebody you know really well, it doesn't need to have a date or the writer's address, it is written in a chatty style, it uses short sentences and simple vocabulary and it ends with just the writer's first name.
5	Point out to the class that newsletters are also used by organisations for advertising purposes and member recruitment. (see p16 for linked work on leaflets)
6	Reinforce the four main structural features of this genre of writing as given on the worksheet, namely: it describes how to carry out a process or procedure, it lists the materials needed to carry out that procedure, it is usually a series of steps in a specific order and it usually contains action verbs. Recipes are a good example of instruction text.
7	Reinforce the basic characteristics of a semi-formal letter, namely: it is only used when writing to someone you know well but don't see very often, it has the writers address and the date, it uses first names, and it has a friendly closing to the main text.
8	Ask the pupils to act out a conversation. For instance, they could pretend to be two teachers talking in the staff room or a famous footballer being interviewed after a match.
9	Reinforce the two main structural features of this genre of writing as given on the worksheet, namely: it focuses on a specific subject or idea and it provides facts, drawings, diagrams and examples to support the subject. You could also point out to the pupils that this style of writing is usually non-chronological.
10	You may like to point out to the class that there are several alternative and perfectly acceptable variations to the basic structure of the formal letter which is outlined on the pupil's worksheet. For example, the date can be written below either the writer's address or the addressee's address and the paragraphs can be indented or set out in block format.
11	Reinforce the main structural features of a paragraph as given on the worksheet. Select a text with paragraphs for the class to look at and discuss where the paragraphs begin and end. Try to avoid text containing dialogue at this stage.
12	Reinforce the three main structural features of this genre of writing as given on the worksheet, namely: it describes how something works, it involves the use of facts and it often describes a series of steps in a specific order. You could also mention to the pupils that explanation text is usually written in the present tense.
13	As a follow-up activity to the worksheet, ask your pupils to try and make up some alliterations of their own, either in separate sentences or in short story form similar to Q3 on the worksheet.
14	Point out to the class that the terms fact and fiction can apply equally well to both the written word and the spoken word. Play 'fact or fiction' by making a statement and asking the pupils to decide which of these two alternatives apply.

15	Reinforce the four main structural features of this genre of writing as given on the worksheet, namely: it uses action verbs, it contains facts and details, it may be personal (involves 'I' and 'we') and it is usually chronological. You could also mention to the pupils that recount text is usually written in the past tense.
16	Collect some specimen leaflets of different types for the class to look at. Discuss the content, layout and purpose of each leaflet with the pupils. Suitable types of leaflets are freely available from libraries, tourist information offices, DIY superstores and other retail outlets. (see also p5 for linked work on newsletters)
17	Take a selection of books to the classroom with blurbs on their covers. Have both fiction and non-fiction. Discuss the content of the blurb and its reasons for being there. Point out to the pupils that a blurb can also be found elsewhere on book covers. Show the pupils an example of this. Take in and let the class look at different types of adverts. Study their content and purpose.
18	Reinforce the main structural features of this genre of writing as given on the worksheet, namely: it has a beginning, a middle and an end, it involves characters (animals or people) and dialogue, it usually presents a problem to solve and it usually ends with a solution to the problem. You could also mention to the pupils that narrative text may be purely fictional or it may also include some information.
19	Before the pupils attempt the worksheet, have an oral session with the class along these lines: ask for ideas about a story. Once agreed, draw a six-box writing frame on the blackboard. Following discussion, sketch in six pictures that are important points in the story. Write one sentence below each picture describing the scene. Then ask the pupils to work independently and combine the sentences with others to create a more detailed version of the story.
20	To complete this worksheet, the pupils also need their completed 'Trouble With the Weather' story from the 'Story boards' worksheet, p19. When pupils have produced their own stories in the normal classroom situation, redrafting can make it look very messy, but writing on alternate lines creates space for changes and means fewer mistakes during rewriting.
21	Reinforce the main structural features of this genre of writing, namely: it is usually written in the 1st person (for further activities dealing with 1st and 2nd person see Unit 2, Bk B, p6) and it should be in roughly chronological order. You could also point out to the pupils that an autobiography needs to be a true account of the happenings in a person's life.
22	Point out to the class that the writing frame used on this worksheet is only for narrative text and that frames for other text-types have different questions. For the Check-up Test for this sheet in Book D the pupil needs to have their completed worksheet to refer to.
23	Give the class further information about the term 'editing.' Explain that it is mainly a publishing term and takes place after drafting (see p20 for work on drafting) and before proof-reading (see p25 for work on proof-reading).
24	Reinforce the main structural features of this genre of writing, namely: it is usually written in the 3rd person, it is a form of recount text (for further activities dealing with recount text see p15) and it should be in roughly chronological order. Also mention that a biography should be a true account.
25	Give the class further information about the term 'proof-reading.' Explain that it is mainly a publishing term and takes place after editing (see p23 for work on editing), and immediately before final publication.
26	Even though most e-mails are written informally, point out to the pupils how important it is to bear in mind who is likely to be reading an e-mail, and to write it appropriately.
27	Point out to the class that there are many different styles of poetry text. Lyric (involving the poet's emotions and feelings) and narrative (telling of stories) are among the most common. Impress on the pupils that most styles use word pictures to build sensory impressions and create images and play with the sounds of words and the rhythms of phrases.